Off Hours

CARTOONS BY JEAN WATTS

BOOK COVER DESIGN BY MARK SORAH/ART DIRECTION, 513 278-4254

Published by Ohio Psychology Press
P.O. Box 90095, Dayton, Ohio 45490
Copyright © 1992

Library of Congress Cataloging-in-Publication Data

Watts, Jean, 1949-
    Off hours / by Jean Watts.
        p.   cm.
    ISBN 0-910707-20-0:
    1. American wit and humor, Pictorial.   I. Title.

NC1429.W248A4   1992
741.5'973 — dc20   91-44156
                                                    CIP

Dedication

To Pat, Jim, Jo, Edie, Joan and the staff and students of Glenburn Elementary School who fill all my hours with moments to remember . . . and to my family, the best anyone could ask for. Thanks, guys.

FOREWORD

The talent of creativity is difficult to define, though we usually can recognize creativity when we see it. The same can be said for the talent of humor in cartoons, only more so.

Jean Watts possesses both great talents in large amounts. Her views of life around her are refreshing, novel, and insightful, and her cartoons help us maintain a sense of perspective and humor in a world that badly needs both.

In her first book, *In Search of Perspective,* Jean Watts focused on the grins and groans of parenting and teaching gifted, talented, creative children. At that time I commented "What Doonesbury did for college students, what Charlie Brown did for everyman, Jean Watts is doing for gifted children, their parents and teachers."

In *Off Hours,* Jean Watts has broadened her scope. Her visions of everyday life again provide fresh perspectives. Her cartoons describe our own feelings — often ones we *wish* we could let ourselves express — about our jobs, parenting, travel, or just balancing the many pushes and pulls in our lives.

Jean Watts is a rare find. A virtual unknown until recently, I believe she is here to stay. I hope Jean will keep on producing her cartoons in the same insightful fashion. She is carving out her own niche in the field.

Jean Watts' *Off Hours* is an excellent book. I recommend it highly for your enjoyment.

> Mike Peters,
> Pulitzer Prize-winning
> Editorial Cartoonist and
> Creator, *Mother Goose and Grimm*

"SAYS HERE THEY'RE GOING TO TAX SALT, SUGAR, FAT AND ANYTHING WITH AN SPF OR R FACTOR LESS THAN 20."

"NO MATTER WHAT THEY DO OR TRY, ANYONE OVER TWELVE STILL LOOKS ELDERLY TO ME."

"SINCE PASSION IS THE BEST PREDICTOR OF FUTURE PROMISE, WE HAVE NO PROBLEM CHOOSING THIS YEAR'S WINNER..."

"TEACHING IS A VERY SOLITARY PROFESSION," SHE THOUGHT, "ALL BUT THE KID PART."

"WHY CAN'T TEACHING BE LIKE PLAYING CARDS... YOU TAKE WHAT YOU'RE DEALT, BUT YOU GET TO DISCARD ONE?"

"BUT HOW WILL I KNOW IF MY A'S ARE STRAIGHT?"

POST INDUSTRIAL NOMADIC NOSTALGIA

"CLASS, TRUST ME. GET TO KNOW YOUR AREA IN DEPTH BEFORE YOU ATTEMPT TO BE CREATIVE."

"MISS BUZZARD, I HAVE HERE IN MY NOTES THAT ON THREE SEPARATE OCCASIONS YOU DID ADMIT THE DEFENDANT HAD POTENTIAL."

"ONLY TWO CARRY ONS ALLOWED...WHICH PIECE WILL YOU BE CHECKING?"

"BUT HOW WILL WE MOTIVATE THEM NEXT YEAR," THEY THOUGHT.

DAD WAS QUIET
BUT EDUCATIONALLY SUPPORTIVE.

TEACHER CHEERLEADERS

"NOW, WHOEVER THINKS OF A METAPHOR FOR TOXIC WASTE FIRST CAN PITCH."

"I'D BETTER WATCH THIS STRESS," JANE SUPPOSED, "OR THE NEXT THING I KNOW I'll LOSE MY MIND TOO."

"IF I CAN'T RECALL THEIR NAMES, HOW WILL I CLASSIFY THEM ALPHABETICALLY? THERE MUST BE A BETTER WAY", YOUNG LINNEUS THOUGHT.

"I TAKE IT YOU STILL NEED THAT PLANNING PERIOD."

"I CAN'T BELIEVE YOU ALLOW THEM TO PLAY INDISCRIMINATELY ON WORDS LIKE THAT."

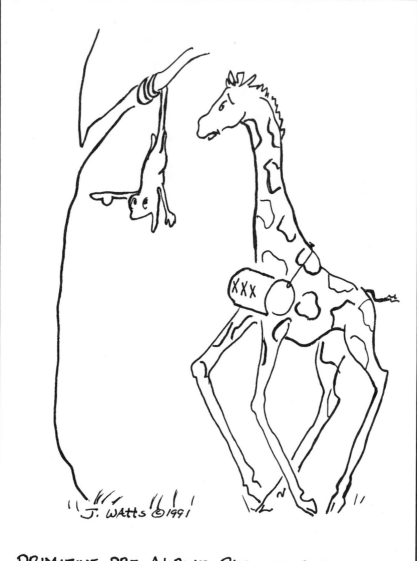

PRIMITIVE PRE-ALPINE RESCUE GIRAFFES

GATES
101 – 125
BAGGAGE CLAIM
BOOKS
CANDY
EXPENSIVE GIFTS
THAT LOOK LIKE
YOU SHOPPED
TACKY GIFTS
WITH CITY
NAMES
J. WATTS © 1991

"WHOOPS, FORGOT TO PUT YOU PEOPLE ON THE SCHEDULE. WHY DON'T YOU JUST COME BACK SOME OTHER DAY?"

"DADDY, WATCH! I'M GONNA MAKE YOU A HOUSE, A CAR AND THE WHOLE ACROPOLIS!"

OSCAR FELT THE ARGUMENT HAD BEEN
PREMATURELY CLOSED.

"GO ON NOW... IF WE DON'T PUT HIM UP THERE
WHO WILL? THE SOONER THE BETTER I SAY."

"MY! WHAT GREAT BIG
TEACHER BAGS YOU HAVE!"

"ONLY A PERSON WITH NO THIRD GRADE
SYMPATHIES COULD HAVE SPELLED 'OUGH'
WORDS THIS WAY."

"SINCE WE APPEAR TO HAVE REACHED AN IMPASSE IN NEGOTIATIONS, I MOVE WE GO TO EXECUTIVE SESSION."

"THANK YOU FOR SHARING THAT WITH US, BILLY."

"IT'S NOT MATH ANXIETY... JUST GIVE
ME A MINUTE... MY NAME WILL COME TO ME."

"NOW THIS MODEL WILL OPEN ONLY IF YOU CAN PROVE YOU'VE HAD LESS THAN 50 GRAMS OF FAT THAT DAY!"

"SILLY DADDY... I NOT WON... I THREE!"

"LOOK – IT'S MY JOB TO SEND THE CREDIT CARD PROTECTION OFFERS. YOU CHECK THE MAIL FOR REJECTIONS, THEN ONLY MUG THOSE."

"MOM, I WAS ONLY HAVING A DIALOGUE BUT HE WAS HAVING A QUARREL."

REMBRANDT CLUNG THERE; HIS WHOLE CHILDHOOD FLASHING BEFORE HIS EYES.

"I'M NOT SURE. WHAT DO YOU THINK?
AM I DECISIVE?"

THE ROCKING CHAIRS ADDED A RHYTHM TO HER OTHERWISE BUSY LIFE.

"I SUGGESTED YOU ADD RIGOR TO YOUR LESSONS, NOT RIGOR MORTIS."

"RUN EVERYBODY! THE MATH TEST MONSTER.!"

"HARD TO RELAX TILL YOU'RE HOME, HUH."

"DONCHA JUST MEET THE WIERDEST TYPES WHEN YOU TRAVEL?.. YOU ON BUSINESS, SIR? ME TOO... WHY THE STORIES I HAVE TO TELL YOU..."

REPORT
MATH B+
SPELLING B
ENGLISH A-
HISTORY B+
MUSIC A-
ED B+
CARD
HOW TO CLEAN TOILETS D+
MAKE COOKIES C+
CHANGE CAR OIL D
PUT TILE DOWN
DOING CHARITIES C
QUIET CRANKY BABY D
NOT UNDERMINE SPOUSE F
ORGANIZE CLOSETS D
DEVELOP A CALLING D-
J. Watts © 1991

"LOOKS LIKE A LONG DELAY, GERALD."

"THIS BOATING STUFF WOULD MAKE A LOT MORE SENSE IF I COULD SEE HOW IT ALL FITS TOGETHER FIRST."

"THAT WON'T HELP, NANA. MY BOTTOM
DOESN'T HAVE EARS."

"...AND THE CLOTH UNIT IS FOR MY PARENTS
TO PUNCH WHEN THEY'RE UPSET."

"OH NO!.. DON'T TELL THE PILOT ABOUT THE HUGE HOLE... HE'LL THINK I DID IT!"

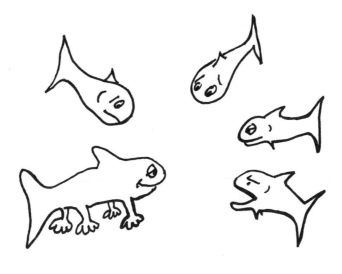

"BE REALISTIC. YOU GRADUATED LAST IN SWIM SCHOOL. IF NONE OF US HAVE MADE IT ON SHORE YET, HOW COULD YOU?"

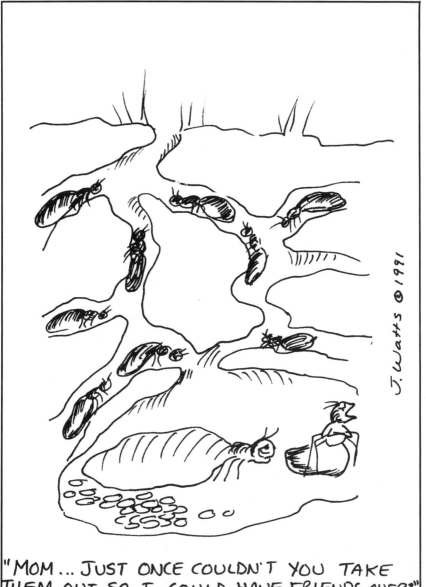

"MOM... JUST ONCE COULDN'T YOU TAKE THEM OUT SO I COULD HAVE FRIENDS OVER?"

"AH...THERE'S NOTHING LIKE THE EARLY MORNING SQUEAK OF ROLLER BALL PENS AT TOP SPEED."

"SINCE YOU ASKED, IT'S THE WORM WHO WAS GOING TO ST. LOUIS BUT WAS DISTRACTED BY A BAND OF ALIEN RABID ARMADILLOS HE HAD TO SLIME BEFORE HE FINISHED TRYING TO EAT DIRT FOR THE PLANTS EVEN THOUGH HE PROMISED THEM FIRST BECAUSE THEIR ROOTS WERE SORE FROM ACID RAIN."

"NOW THAT TEACHER PAY HAS IMPROVED, I CAN SPEND A LOT MORE ON MY CLASSROOM."

"SO, WHICH OF SOCIETY'S NEEDS DO YOU PLAN TO FULFILL?"

"WHAT DO YOU MEAN I HAVE TO EXPLAIN HOW I GOT HERE FROM THERE OR IT DOESN'T COUNT?"

"ACTUALLY, I WAS HOPING TO EMPTY MY MIND OF THIS STUFF ONCE I GET HOME SO I CAN THINK."

BACK TO BASICS

"WILL YOU BE USING OUR NEW CUSTOMER HIBERNATION SERVICE?"

"DEBBIE NEVER WINS ANY POPULARITY CONTESTS, BUT YOU HAVE TO ADMIT, SHE'S CREATIVE!"

"OH, WE HAD A GREAT PROGRAM LAST YEAR BUT SHE MOVED."

"WELL, COME TO THINK OF IT, I HAVE NOTICED THE FASTER I LEARN, THE SMALLER I FEEL, THE MORE WEIGHT MY OPINIONS CARRY AND THE LESS I REMEMBER THE TIME."

"WELL, IF GRADES WERE DONE BY LOTTERY, I'D SAY YOU WOULD HAVE A FIGHTING CHANCE."

"HERE, HAVE ANOTHER COMIC BOOK...
THEY'RE STILL ARGUING ABOUT HOW TO
IMPROVE THE SCHOOLS."

ANGELA FOUND VELCRO WAS THE
ANSWER TO HER DISTRACTIBILITY

"DON'T WORRY. THEY ONLY PRETEND TO LISTEN TO US ANYHOW."

"HE'S HEAD AND SHOULDERS ABOVE THE OTHERS IN CLASS, BUT FRANKLY I'M CONCERNED ABOUT HIS FINE MOTOR SKILLS."

"MOM IRONS STANDING UP, NOT BY JUST RESTING ON IT LIKE YOU DO, DAD."

"YOU FINDING IT DIFFICULT TO MAINTAIN YOUR ASPIRATIONS?"

"SOME OF YOU MAY NOT KNOW WE HAVE A NEW FOREIGN EXCHANGE STUDENT!"

"YOUNG MAN! BACK TO YOUR DESK TO FINISH THAT DISTANCE/RATE PROBLEM!"

OAKLY WAS FINISHED EARLY AND APPEARED
BORED.

"THIS IS YOUR CAPTAIN AGAIN... YOU'LL
NOTICE A SPECTACULAR VIEW OF THE
OZONE HOLE TO YOUR UPPER LEFT... WELL
IT FIGURES... NOBODY'S LISTENING TO ME..."

"MRS. GARDNER, WE'RE REALLY PRESSED FOR TIME. COULDN'T WE JUST SAY WE DID THE PART ON ETHICS?"

"OH, SHE'S JUST USING THAT FRESH MUD TO MAKE AN IMPRESSION BUT HOW LONG DO YOU THINK THAT WILL LAST?"

"I DON'T THINK YOU KIDS REALIZE HOW MUCH YOUR MOTHER CRAVES SOLITUDE."

"LORRAINE? APPARENTLY THE NEW STATE REGULATIONS ARE HERE."

"I SUPPOSE THE PHRASE 'A IS FOR APPLE' MEANS NOTHING TO YOU."

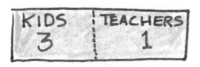

"... OH, YES, BUT THEN WE DON'T WORRY ABOUT THE TRAFFIC WITH A HOUSE GIRAFFE."

"YOU NEVER HEAR MAST SUPPORT OR ROCK SUPPORT ANYMORE... THE PIER SUPPORT GUYS MUST HAVE A BIGGER AD BUDGET."

"YOUNG MAN, I AM THROUGH RECOMBINING GENES FOR YOU IF YOU CONTINUE TO INSIST ON MUTATING IN THERE."

"OH SURE, IT LOOKS GOOD... BUT THE NEAREST MALL IS 87 MILES, REMEMBER?"

"SOMETIMES I THINK YOU LIKE THAT DOG MORE
THAN YOU DO ME...WELL, DOES HE WANT CREAM
OR NOT, CHARLES?"

"REMEMBER, TEACHERS, YOUR FINAL EXAM WILL BE IN 40 YEARS WHEN WE CHECK TO SEE HOW YOUR STUDENTS DID IN LIFE."

"IN REFLECTION, I SHOULD PROBABLY HAVE CHOSEN MY PEERS WITH MORE CARE."

"I TAKE IT SHE WAS NOT A GOOD
PRODUCT OF THE SYSTEM."

"YES, I HAVE ASPIRATIONS AND ITS NOT TO BE COLORING YELLOW CHICKIES."

"MOM? WHAT MAKES A FOREST PETRIFIED?"

"OF ALL THE PRIME CANDIDATES THE ONE ON THE LEFT SEEMS TO BE THE EXCEPTIONAL ONE."

"LADIES AND GENTLEMEN... WE WILL BEGIN BOARDING AS SOON AS WE ARE ABLE TO OBTAIN A FLIGHT CREW."

"OH, HE'S NO THREAT TO US TONIGHT, KID, THE OLD BAT JUST HAD HIS WINGS PERMED."

NOT WANTING TO INSTILL GUILT, SHE BALANCED CHILD and JOB WITH OUTWARD CALM.

"I RECEIVED A LOT OF INNER SATISFACTION FROM THAT KID."

"LOOK... THE MALE CELLS HAVE SOME SCHEME TO EVOLVE US INTO HUNTERS. I SAY WE HOLD OUR DNA 'TILL WE GET GATHERING AND KIDS."

THE SUGGESTION OF FURTHER BUDGET CUTS
WAS MET WITH BRAVE SMILES BY MOST.

"OH...YOU'RE RIGHT...SILLY ME...'MAKE A DECISION' COMES AFTER 'CONSIDER THE CONSEQUENCES'."

"TEN BUCKS IF YOU'LL TAKE MY CAFETERIA DUTY WITH THEM NOW."

"PSST... GOT THE TRUCK? I'VE GOT THE DOLL. THINK ANYONE SAW US?"

"SHHH...NOW ACT INNOCENT...DON'T LET THEM KNOW I'VE FILLED YOU IN..."

"JOAN... COULDN'T YOU HAVE BOUGHT HIM THE KIND OF SHOES CHESS PLAYERS WEAR THIS TIME?"

"...BURT, THIS FIRST SECTION OF DNA CODE TRANSLATES...' IN CASES OF DIFFICULTY WITH THIS MODEL CONTACT MANUFACTURER AT ONCE."

"...NO, THIS ONE SHOULD FIT MY CURRICULUM JUST FINE. IT'S 40 MINUTES LONG."

YOUR TEACHER WILL BE RIGHT BACK AFTER THIS PAUSE...
1 +2 4
4 x3 6
7 −1 4
3 +2 6
7 +2 11
7 +2 10
J WATTS © 1991

AS LONG THEORIZED, ON MARCH 8th A NEW
LIFE FORM BEGAN TO EMERGE FROM
JASON'S SIXTH GRADE DESK.

"MY GRANDMOTHER SAYS IF YOU HOLD IT TO
YOUR EAR...WHY, BY GOLLY, SHE'S RIGHT...
YOU CAN HEAR A BASKETBALL GAME!"

"LOOK—WE CAME HERE TO NEGOTIATE NOT TO LOOK FOR TRUTH."

CLAUDIA GREW TIRED OF TRYING TO GRASP ALL
THOSE EPHEMERAL IDEAS SHE HAD, SO SHE
DROVE TO THE LOCAL 'SHOP N' DROP' TO BUY
AN 'ENQUIRER'S UPDATE' AND A TWINKIE-POP.

"WE WERE JUST DEEPENING AND BROADENING OUR CAPACITY FOR SELF-DISCLOSURE, SIR."

"IT'S NOT FAIR. WE ALWAYS HAVE TO DO EVERYTHING."

"... WHY NOT ADJUST YOUR PACE? LOOKS TO ME LIKE YOU'RE THE ONLY ONE IN THAT RACE, LADY."

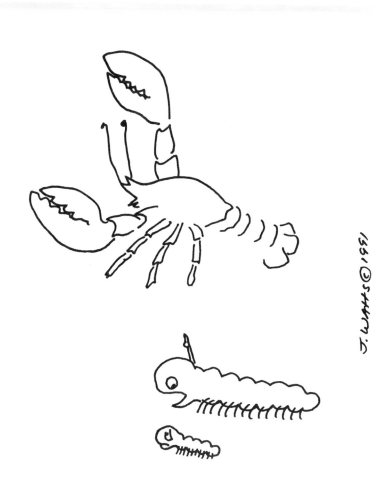

"SON, WHY CAN'T YOU DEVELOP LIKE HE DID AND GIVE YOURSELF SOME REAL CLOUT IN LIFE?"

"YOU SEE, IN TONGA, POWER AND RANK ARE BASED ON A COMPLICATED SYSTEM OF LINEAGE, KINSHIP, HIERARCHY AND MATRILINEAL CUSTOMS, WHEREAS IN A DEMOCRACY LIKE OURS WE GO BY LOOKS."

"...AND THE NEXT TIME MY KID IS GOING TO
FLUNK A TEST, I WANT TO BE NOTIFIED
IN ADVANCE."

" 'HYPE, NON-COMPLEX, INFLEXIBLE WITH CLOSURE'... YUP... PERFECT FOR VEGGING."

JESSIE'S INVENTIONS WERE NOT RANDOM,
BUT HER DEBRIS NEEDED SOME HELP.

"WE CAN PLAY QUIETLY LATER... MOM NEEDS US NOW... SHE'S TALKING TO THAT PLASTIC THING AGAIN... HURRY!"

"HEY !!... CAN HE DO THAT ?"

"OH...I'VE HEARD THAT EDITION OF WEBSTER IS SO GOOD. PERSONALLY I LIKE A LITTLE MORE SLANG THOUGH...YOU ALONE, SIR ?"

"ROUTINE, SIR,..WE RECHECK ANYTHING UNUSUAL. MAY I SEE THAT BRIEFCASE AGAIN PLEASE?"

"AT LAST...LAUNDRY'S DONE...THE KIDS AT CAMP...THE FIRST SOLITUDE IN MONTHS."

"HE WAS PERFECTLY CONTENT UNTIL SOME DO-GOODER DEFINED 'CAGE' FOR HIM."

"NOW HERE WE HAVE AN EXAMPLE OF VERBAL INERTIA...OBJECTS THAT ARE SILENT TEND TO REMAIN SO, WHILE OBJECTS THAT VERBALIZE TEND TO KEEP RIGHT ON VERBALIZING."

"WHASSA MATTER... MOMMY WON'T LET YOU
EAT ARTIFICIAL INGREDIENTS?"

"OH FOR PETE'S SAKE, I HAVE GOT TO SLOW DOWN. I'VE PUT MY MAKEUP ON UPSIDE DOWN AGAIN."

"OK, LET'S SEE IF I'VE GOT THIS... DAD WILL MOW, DON DOES TRASH, WENDY...DISHES, KATE WILL VACUUM, AND I'LL SHUT BUREAU DRAWERS, WIPE TOOTHPASTE BLOBS, PICK UP SOCKS, SCOUR DOG DISHES, SHUT OFF CELLAR LIGHTS, SCRUB THE TOILET AND RECYCLE REFRIGERATOR REMAINS."

IN HORROR, HE SAW THE LOGIC OF IT. IF
PTERODACTYLS BECAME BIRDS, WHAT WAS
TO STOP THAT SOCK FROM EVOLVING, AS
HE WATCHED, INTO A VAMPIRE.

BY LAMINATING HERSELF SHE HOPED TO LAST THROUGH THE YEAR WITH THIS CLASS.

"THOUGH YOUR ARGUMENT WAS FALLACIOUS, INCONSISTENT AND BASED ON WORTHLESS EVIDENCE, YOU SAID IT IN A REALLY NICE WAY."

"YOU DON'T SERIOUSLY EXPECT TO COME UP
WITH A PROPOSAL ONE OF MY STATURE WILL
ACCEPT DO YOU?"

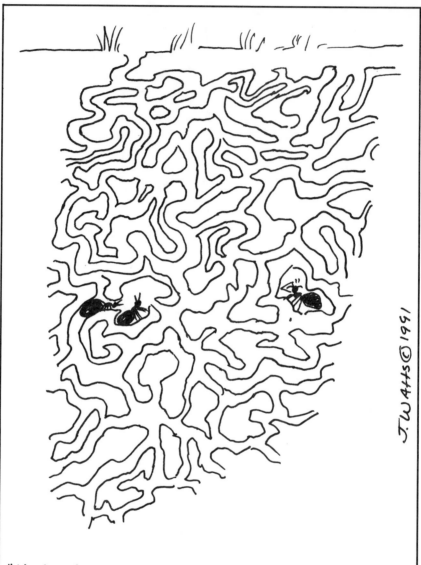

"HARLEY, CALL THE TOPOLOGIST. HOWARD'S LOST AGAIN."

"SAM—TELL THE COMMITTEE THEY'RE NOT PUTTING THIS ONE ON THE BACK BURNER."

"I'M BORED. THERE'S NOTHING TO DO."

"SO, IF MY SON IS ON THE LOW END OF HYPERACTIVITY, I INSIST YOU GET HIM UP TO THE LEVEL OF THE OTHER KIDS."

"MOM!!..,THE FRIG IS BALD!!"

J. Watts © 1991

"MOM.. HOW ABOUT LOOKING AT THIS AS A KIND OF REPORT-CARD-BUILDING YEAR."

"HE WAS NICE ENOUGH TO COME ALL THIS WAY
SO, CLASS, LET'S REMEMBER TO ACT POLITELY
WHEN OUR GUEST SPEAKER ARRIVES."

"HE'LL NEVER LET US GO. DAD'S PHILOSOPHY
IS 'I DID, THEREFORE I KNOW.'"

"IT'S MONDAY.
LET ME PUT MY COAT DOWN FIRST."

"I DON'T CARE IF YOU HAVE RESOLVED THE GREAT EXTINCTION PROBLEM... IF THAT ROOM ISN'T CLEAN IN 10 MINUTES, YOUNG MAN, YOU'VE HAD IT!"

"LET ME GET THIS STRAIGHT...YOU WANT
ME TO STOP HANGING OUT, READ BOOKS FOR
ABOUT 10 MORE YEARS, SO I CAN IMPRESS
SOME PEOPLE WHO DON'T LIKE ME NOW BY
DOING SOMETHING I NEVER HEARD OF ?"

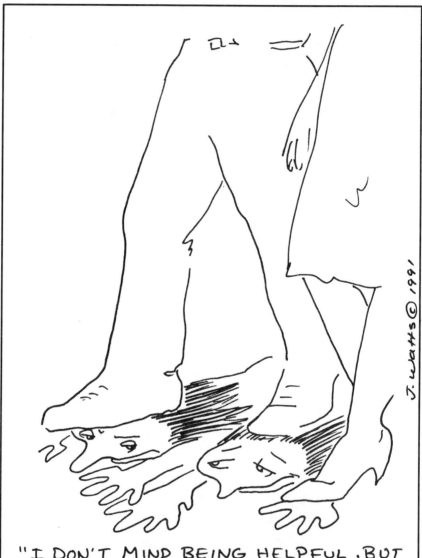

"I DON'T MIND BEING HELPFUL, BUT DO YOU THINK THEY'LL REMEMBER US WITHOUT EYE CONTACT?"

BUZZY SPENT SO MUCH TIME FINDING THE
LOOPHOLES HE FAILED TO NOTICE THE SYSTEM.

©J.WAHS 1941

"BUT YOU HAVE TO ADMIT..IT IS POSSIBLE
TO AMOUNT TO SOMETHING AND JUST NOT
HAVE ANYONE KNOW IT, RIGHT?"

"YOU GUYS, WE'VE GOT TO FIND A ROLE MODEL, SOMEONE LARGER THAN LIFE TO TAKE US IN, SO TO SPEAK."

"BUT... WHERE'S THE TOILET TRAIN?"

"PICASSO, HONEY, LET'S BE A BIT LESS SHOWY NOW AND LET THE OTHERS BE NOTICED."

Biography

Jean Watts lives in Maine with her husband, four children, two dogs and two cats, where she teaches gifted and talented students and often wonders if there is life after dog hair and laundry. She has a Masters of Education degree from the University of Maine and enjoys conducting workshops at national conferences where other people cook. Jean is also the author of the widely acclaimed *In Search of Perspective.*